The Lonely Dreamer

David Clark

NEWMAN SPRINGS PUBLISHING
320 Broad Street
Red Bank, NJ 07701

First originally published by Newman
Springs Publishing 2024

ISBN 979-8-89061-902-0 (Paperback)
ISBN 979-8-89061-903-7 (Digital)

Printed in the United States of America

Let's Write

When I was young, I had a long list of occupations I thought might interest me. The list included surgeon, airline pilot, and ballet dancer, and it did not include engineer, which is what I became, nor writer, which, if you read on, you might decide would not have been the best choice. Not that I'm a bad writer; I'm just not prolific enough. I don't wake up in the morning thinking about what I'll write that day.

But in second grade we had a unit at the end of each school day using a workbook called *Let's Write*. I hated it at first, so I was surprised to find by the end of the school year that I enjoyed it. *Let's Write* was about grammar and spelling and not about composition, but it gave me the feeling that writing could be rewarding.

Decades went by, and I pursued other interests, not to mention attempts at maintaining a career in a technical field, and creative writing was not always at the top of my mind. At the office I did the sort of writing engineers do, full of tables and graphs and dispassionate discourse, and I got good at it, but that was a very structured style that allowed little opportunity to let the mind wander.

And then one day, sitting at my desk and struggling to focus on the task at hand, my mind did begin to wander. I don't remember where the idea came from, but I started to experiment with a stream-of-consciousness story about a toad and a fox who work in an office and bicker across the cubicle wall. In a moment of self-flattery I told myself it was a clever story, except I couldn't figure out how to end it, so years later I made up an ending just so I could include it in this book. But I write because it allows me to invent new worlds, and other themes have come to mind over the years, so read on…

Grumpy Old Animals

"This is really dumb," said the green toad to the red fox. "In the general scheme of things, this is a really inefficient way of doing business." Truly, the world has advanced to a high degree when toads begin to worry about efficiency in business.

Anyway, Fox took that as a hint and began to clean his office. He found all kinds of things he had forgotten he had. As he uncovered layer after layer of stuff he had accumulated, he went further and further back in memory until he found the earliest toy he could remember, which was his rattle. He began to wonder how his toys got in his office.

Then Fox began to wonder if Toad had put all that stuff there when he wasn't looking just to make him clean it up. That thought began to eat at him as he piled all his stuff in a big box, and the more he thought about it, the more he wanted to quit cleaning and put it all back the way it used to be just to spite the toad.

3

So after spending all day trying to straighten up his office, Fox did put it all back just as it was before, and his office was even more cluttered than before he began. Toad came by just at five, looked in, and turned red. (A green toad with a red face is quite a sight).

He said, "Fox, you have been cleaning all day, and it's still just as messy as it was this morning. What have you been doing? Drinking coffee all day, trying to fool us?"

Fox replied, "Just what you've been doing all these years, messing up my office a little at a time, so you could make me clean it up!" Fox, fortunately, was already red in color, and the additional redness in his face didn't show, so Toad thought he was kidding.

Fox thought that Toad was sort of an ugly, squat, pompous little fellow who scowled all the time. He was so small, but he thought himself so important. It was infuriating. He just wanted to grab the toad by the neck and shake him and throw him out of the office. He would have too if he'd had a neck. But Toad had the sort of glib personality that made people feel intimidated, and Fox was afraid to stand up to him even though he was bigger and could run faster and was, after all, better-looking.

So Fox spent his working days frustrated at his inability to deal with the personality of Toad. Toad was just such a pushy sort, always trying to be the boss. It didn't really eat him up, it wasn't that bad, but every time he passed Toad in the hall he tried not to catch his eye.

Toad, on the other hand, couldn't understand why no one liked him. Everyone seemed to be so curt, always giving short answers and crossing the hall to avoid him. He also couldn't understand why nobody did things the way he thought they should be done. In his delusions about himself he thought his way was just so logical. For instance, that Fox, he couldn't keep his office neat if you threatened to confiscate his coffee cup, which Toad sometimes wanted to do. And he was such a ninny, always whining "Why do they keep doing this to me?" Toad never thought about what *this* was and who *they* were.

Toad always thought people needed leadership. They were all such sheep, never having any ideas of their own, always doing what everyone else did, saying the same things, even walking the same way. They always laughed at the same jokes they had heard every day since time began. He told himself that he, at least, always thought for himself, never accepting others' ideas without first applying creative and out-of-the-box thought. He thought of himself as superior, a better worker, more effective, deserving more respect. He said to himself, "That's why I don't get treated with respect—they're jealous." He would refuse to associate with them. They were so far beneath him.

Take Fox. He worked all day to clean his office, and it didn't get cleaned. He just wanted to walk into Fox's office and throw everything away; that would show him! Toad would have cleaned it in a half hour and had the rest of the day to do other things, productive things that would make everyone respect him. That was just the problem—he never got an opportunity to do something easy that would get the quick recognition like the others always did.

Fox thought of himself as perhaps not quite good enough, but he didn't really know that he thought that; he just went through life with doubts about himself. Toad told himself he was the best because his mother had always said he was. So Fox and Toad went on about their jobs, each thinking badly about the other.

Then one day, something happened. It started off as a normal day—start work at eight, lunch at twelve, walk to the Xerox, get coffee, stop and talk to your friends in the halls, get more coffee. Fox played with his computer to put off a project he was supposed to do. Toad sat in his office with a scowl, reading a magazine, wondering why no one else did as much work as he did. Three came, and both of them looked at the clock every five minutes, hoping some diversion would come along to make five come faster.

About three thirty Fox noticed that the hallway near the window was not as bright as it had been, and he went to check it out. Dark clouds had gathered, looking very much like a storm was coming. As he looked out, lightning flashed a distance away—a long, fat, posthole digger, like the ones that used to frighten him so when he was just a kit living in his mother's den on the hillside. A loud bang came a few seconds later, followed by reverberating bumps and rumbles. An old fear came to him as he remembered the storms that frightened him when he was young.

The bright flash attracted Toad's attention because where he sat, he could see down the hallway. He was offended to see Fox standing there looking out the window when there was work to do and decided that he would not go look himself; he was going to show Fox how a good worker should behave, by golly! The loud bang that came shortly after the flash reminded Toad that work must come before entertainment. So he continued to sit at his desk, reading the magazine and feeling righteous.

Toad began to write a letter to his mother, who was his best friend because she always told him that toads were the greatest of all and that he was the greatest toad. As he wrote, he was dimly aware that the storm was getting closer and noisier. He heard someone speak in the hall, and he became aware of a whining sound. But he told himself he was too hard-working to look up. If they wanted to watch a stupid storm, let them get in trouble. He would work hard and get credit.

A few minutes later, Toad looked down the hall again and noticed that Fox was not at the window. He felt peeved at this because he couldn't feel quite as superior to Fox when he couldn't see him goofing off.

Suddenly, as Toad was writing a sentence to his mother about the other office people who were slackers, there was a loud noise and the walls of his office shook. Boards fell all around him, and Toad suddenly found himself sitting under his desk in the dark with rubble all around, trapped in the debris with no way of getting out.

Hours went by. It happened that Toad was a huge glutton, and he loved spaghetti with meatballs, and he began to get hungry, but there was nothing to eat. He called out, but no one answered. His mind was filled with thoughts of spaghetti, and he especially thought about meatballs.

Just then, a cricket hopped by. Without thinking, Toad put out his tongue and caught the cricket and started chewing. It didn't taste like spaghetti, but he was surprised that he liked it. Toad didn't grow up among other toads, so he didn't know that crickets are the natural food for his kind. It had a pleasant crunchiness and tasted like salted peanuts. He thought, *Not bad, but spaghetti is better.*

Many more hours went by, and Toad had eaten many crickets before he finally heard voices. Someone was pulling away the boards that had fallen around his desk. As he was finishing the last of the crickets there was a glimmer of light, and Fox's face suddenly appeared in the opening. Despite the bright light behind, Toad could tell Fox was grinning. As much as a fox can grin, that is.

Fox said with a laugh, "Toad, your office is a mess!"

Puppy

I'm lying on the floor; the day's work is done.
Or, at least I'm putting off till tomorrow
Things I didn't need to do today.

There's a small sniffing sound in my ear.
A little nose nuzzles my hair.
A little pink tongue takes liberty with my cheek,
And the fur around her muzzle makes me tickle.
With puppylike energy,
A little brown furry head pushes against my side,
Then snuggles into the crook of my shoulder.
She puts her paws on my chest,
And I rub her back.

I stand up because it's suppertime.
She finds a toy and plays while I fix her food,
Pretending she's defeating a fearsome enemy.
The food disappears almost in one swallow,
With cute grunts and snorts.

THE LONELY DREAMER

When I eat, she begs like a pro,
Probably because she finds that it works.

Then it's outside to chase a ball
And sometimes a rabbit.
We have coyotes and eagles,
So she's too small to put outside by herself.
I have to wait with her till she makes lemonade
And a Tootsie Roll;
Otherwise, she'll do it in the house.

When I get home from somewhere,
She squeals and puts her paws up on me.
It's funny how animals are friendly and affectionate,
How another species can live among us
As a member of the family.

Quickly she'll grow,
But she won't get much bigger.
She's a small breed,
Known for affection and energy.
Everyone who knows her
Wants to pick her up and hold her.

Maybe I should get another
To keep her company when I'm not here.

The Specialist

Clarantze Blankton, technical linguistic specialist first class (TLS-1, that is), arrived at work one morning to find that his job was leaving him.

Clarantze had worked for Sckullen-Craasbeaune Computer Corporation for seventeen years when that affliction that affects all aging computer companies came around: obsolescence and complacency had reduced the company to bankruptcy. He was so surprised. He was so good at his work, and they were such a team—how could this be happening?

Maybe it isn't really happening, he thought. *I'll just wait to make sure.*

Full of optimism and assuming his value as a writer must be obvious to anyone he spoke with, he waited till the end of the last day of his eight-week notice before he faced the truth and started looking. His first stop was at an obvious place for a man skilled in words—the local newspaper. Judging by some of the language he had read in it lately, it was obvious they could use a solid man like him. He was so certain of his immense value to that enterprise that he walked in without an appointment, acting like a little prince.

"Mr. Blankton—" said the editor.

"Call me Clar," said Clarantze.

"It's such a shame what happened to you all. So hard! So many of you, and after so many years! Anyway, tell me about yourself. How long were you with S Triple C, and what did you do there?"

Clarantze felt a surge of pride as he responded, "I was a technical linguistic specialist, a TLS, as they called us, senior level, and if you don't mind me saying so myself, I was pretty good at what I did."

"What sort of things did you write?"

"I was in the section that did the technical manuals for the disk drives. Our team was responsible for some of the maintenance documentation, most specifically air-filter replacement. We were a big team but a real team! No one was better than us! Not even the team in charge of disc-pack manuals."

"Interesting. And you knew your area quite well, I suppose."

"Yes, the air filters are of the greatest importance. The heads fly unbelievably close to the disc—it's like a 747 flying an inch off the ground. One farmhouse, even one stone, and *bam*, crash and burn! Instant data destruction." He struck his fists together as if to demonstrate the violence of such a cataclysm. "Dust is like a farmhouse to the read head. Real bummer. Happens sometimes."

"Yes, I know…tell me more. What did you do, specifically?"

Clarantze noticed a small toy airplane on the desk, and he began to make loops and dives with it. "I was the guy who was responsible for the word *and*."

Long pause, leaning forward, look of puzzlement.

"*And*? Just that one word?"

This editor must be really stupid. Explains the bad writing, Clarantze thought, smart enough fortunately not to say it aloud.

"Yes! I'm real good at writing *and*. You can't write that word all day long and all week and all year for seventeen years without getting pretty good at it! You wouldn't believe how often *and* is used!"

Clarantze had been told that emphasizing his experience would make him seem more valuable.

"And you know what? I can write *and* in any font, any style of writing you might want! I know them all. I can type it two hundred times a minute! And I can do that while changing fonts on the fly.

14

Most people don't know that *and* can be typed using just one hand, and the other hand can be used on the mouse to change fonts and move the cursor around and stuff."

Clarantze was getting more and more impressed with himself. He thought, *Wow—I was good! This interviewing thing is a piece of cake—with this sales job, I'll be working tomorrow.* Newspapers, after all, use *and* a lot. He started planning in his mind how much paid vacation he might ask for when he worked for the paper.

He sent the little airplane into a zoom climb. With a knowing smile, he added his clincher, the thing he had been saving until last because it proved his value conclusively. "Sometimes the manuals would come to me first before any of the other words had been put in. That's where the experience factor really paid off!"

"How on earth did you do that—just writing *and* on blank pages?"

Clarantze paused to try to control the feeling of impatience that came over him just then. This guy was so slow, he must be on the verge of getting fired himself. Maybe Clarantze would be hired to replace him! He rolled his eyes a bit as he explained, "SCCC was so big we had a specialist for each of the major words, to make sure it was done right, you see. Of course, there are some words that aren't used very often, and we had special guys who would carry multiple-word loads. They were usually the old-timers who had done all the other words sometime in their lives. And there were real sharp guys who were given some of the words that are used together, like *hard drive* or *men's room*. I'm sure I was going to be one of those except the company went bankrupt. That management is so short-sighted.… All those people, all those years, wasted!"—he added with pride and with great emphasis and strong hand gestures—"wasted, I tell you! Probably they really plan to hire all new people and pay them half as much and give them twice as many words."

Clarantze thought that this show of fire would certainly impress the poor peasant across the desk, but the editor brought him back down from his brief orbit.

"You liked your work?"

"Oh yes, I loved it!" Clarantze was told to sound enthusiastic. "I got so good at it, it gave me a sense of real pride! I love that word! In fact, I worked so fast they were going to give me *or* also and maybe even *if* because *if* isn't used as often in technical manuals, but they hired a new guy right out of journalism school, and they had to give him something so they started him on *or*. I don't know what they teach in writing schools these days. Kid couldn't figure out where to put his word. We had to send the manuals around to him last and just let him fill in the blank spots. The word *if* was assigned to an older man who was retiring soon, so it wasn't available for me yet. But it was coming! And I was still hoping to get *or*, if that new kid didn't catch on. It would have been a big load, carrying two of the most common words, plus *if*, but I knew I could do it!" Clarantze was getting wordy because he thought talking a lot would impress people like this editor by showing awareness and intelligence.

"Well, how…how did you get anything done when you had to call a specialist for every word?" The editor was leaning forward with his elbows on the desk. "I expect my people to use all the words, all the time."

"It took us a month to complete each paragraph, but it was done *right*! We were a team, boy, a real team! We had to plan each paragraph real carefully, but we had the teamwork! And, we could adapt in a jiffy if we found some of the early anticipation wasn't quite right. We were fast, and we were good!" He did a few more loops and brought the airplane in for a neat landing on the desk, and the editor seized it and put it away in a drawer.

Clarantze said, "I just don't understand why they had to lay us all off. Poor management, just plain poor management. We could have told them, but they wouldn't have listened."

The editor suddenly turned away. "Thank you very much, Mr. Blankton. We'll be in touch. Good luck to you."

As Clarantze stood to go, he thought, *A little dumb, nice man though, seemed distracted but obviously impressed.* He thought his deep and enduring skill at the one small thing he thought he did well should be enough to prove his great value. That act with the little airplane—what a stroke of genius! It proved he could be so informal and spontaneous—important attributes for a good newspaper-word man.

Clarantze never heard back from the paper; in fact, he never heard from any of the places he interviewed with. He started to think, *Getting a new job is so hard! I need to try harder at being a charmer. Maybe I should get my own little airplane and carry it in my*

pocket just in case. It never occurred to him to learn any other words.

But he did land a job, eventually. One afternoon on his new job he was selling a hamburger with fries and a cola to an obnoxious little kid when he saw the kid glance at his nametag with a smirk. That's when it came to him. *Maybe no one likes a man with a name like Clarantze…must be because of the way I spell it.* So he started spelling it *Clarents*.

Life in the Shop

It's thirty-five pounds and cold to the touch.
When it's done, it'll be ten, and warm from cutting.
Twenty-five of those pounds will be on the floor
In tiny shavings.
It takes time to remove all that metal.
But the ten pounds that remain
Will look just like the drawing,
Full of little holes and interesting features
That give it the desired function
And, hopefully, a good appearance.
Every good designer thinks about looks
As well as function.

Those who don't do shopwork
Will never understand the mixture of
Reward and stress.
The outcome is rewarding, but one mistake
Can destroy days of work.
Every machinist lives with that fear.

THE LONELY DREAMER

You can't put metal back on that's been removed,
And the tiniest fraction of a fraction is enough.
So we always think twice
Before starting a cut
Or turning a knob on the machine.

But an experienced machinist thinks ahead,
Making few mistakes.
Often the part can be used anyway,
And sometimes a design change
Can accommodate an error.
But we know the error was made, and that worries us
Because the next time, it might really matter.

When you get to the end of a complicated job
And you know it was done well,
Efficiently, and with competence,
You'll look at it with pride of a job well done.
That's what keeps us going.

Surgical Assistant Held

By S. Stimmt for the Rochester Press

Surgical assistant Phairtoux Midlin is in the custody of Rochester Police on charges of assault and battery after allegedly performing unauthorized surgery on a patient at St. Nowhere Hospital.

According to witnesses, Midlin was found cutting off the left ear of elderly patient Dimmy Witless, who had been anesthetized and was being prepared for gall bladder surgery.

Nurse Lauda Marcy-Chile, who reported the alleged unauthorized surgery, said that as the patient was being prepared for the operation she heard Midlin ask the attending physician, prominent surgeon Karl Heintz von der Hutenstaussen, the nature of the operation. She said that Dr. Hutenstaussen replied, "ve ah cuttink off his wight eah, shtupit." She said the doctor then left the room, apparently to scrub, leaving Midlin in the room without supervision. Nurse

Marcy-Chile said that Midlin occasionally angered doctors by attempting to do operations himself. She did not know why he cut off the wrong ear.

Dr. Hutenstaussen, reached at his office for comment late this afternoon, said that Midlin regularly assists in surgery at St. Nowhere, and has always been a reliable assistant. He added after further questioning that he occasionally allows Midlin to "weild das Skalpell," but always under direct supervision.

A spokesperson for the hospital, speaking on condition of anonymity, said that Midlin's personnel file contained references to boastful behavior, including the frequent claim that he was as qualified as any physician to perform surgery. The spokesperson also mentioned that Midlin was recently reprimanded for diagnosing a patient on his own initiative. Reportedly, he had told the patient to "take two aspirin and call me in the morning."

Midlin is scheduled for arraignment next week in Rochester District Court. Prosecutors requested that bail be denied on the basis that Mr. Witless was already hard of hearing.

Colorless

Low-hanging clouds this morning
Match my view of life.
I take the dogs out,
Then I don't see much point in staying up.
The dogs join me again in the bed,
And when I waken later, they've gone somewhere
    else,
Which seems to reinforce my sense of emptiness.
Later, the sun comes out,
But that just makes it muggy.

I have things to do today,
And my escape through dreams is interrupted
And won't return.
One errand seems too many.
My unwritten list of three feels overwhelming.
The thing I look forward to is my morning coffee,
But within twenty minutes, that's done.

THE LONELY DREAMER

I can't just check out—
I don't live only for myself.
I know others depend on me
For physical needs and companionship.
I get along, and it's not all bad,
But I wonder why I'm here.
If this is all there is, what does it matter?

My self-effacing nature has never asked
What I can expect out of life.
I've only thought about what others expect from me.
I no longer have a vision of my own
That can carry me forth.
There are things I'm good at,
But I'm no longer improving those skills.
I do get something from life,
If passively, from those around me,
And that keeps me going for now.
But the future seems merely to be endured.
Jumping off a cliff is always an option,
But that would eliminate the possibility
Of anything better.

Do What You're Afraid Of

I've been on pins and needles all week, alternating minute by minute between happy anticipation and outright panic. It's been like this these last few weeks, but this week it's getting worse because the event I fear is suddenly imminent. It's not nuclear war, impending bankruptcy, divorce, or job loss. It's much worse—it's that on Sunday morning, I've agreed to expose myself to the public with a clarinet, a pianist, and nothing to hide behind but a music stand.

Background: once, as a young adult, someone learned that I played an instrument, and I was invited to play in a church service. I expected I'd be great. Instead, I almost died. I got lightheaded and my vision grayed out, my embouchure collapsed, and I played inadvertent trills because my fingers quivered. I didn't finish the piece I was playing because my knees became too weak to hold me up. As a young adult, I dreamed of having a solo career, but that dream was driven away by the specter of consistent failure.

I've worked on the music for several weeks. I know every semiquaver. I can play it flawlessly and artistically in the isolation of my house, and I know I have the full technical and artistic ability to play well. I try to *visualize* success in performance like all the books say to do, but my visualization always collapses back to a cold fear of unavoidable failure. Why I agreed to this is beyond comprehension—in the weeks I've been preparing, I've seen no possibility of success. Once burned, always afraid of the fire—I feel the way a condemned man must feel on his way to execution. When I accepted the invitation to play a few weeks ago, it seemed far enough in the future that it sounded like fun, but now Sunday is getting close, and I'm second-guessing my commitment to play.

It's like being caught in a vise. I'm squeezed and trapped, and there's no way out. I can't sleep well the night before, but I need the sleep that doesn't come, and when I doze off I have dreams of disaster. I waken before the alarm, unable to sleep again. I've committed to a performance and can't back out without a feeling of betrayal, but going forward is as fearsome as, well, a rock and a hard place.

But they say do the thing you're afraid of.

It's now Sunday morning. After a night of insufficient sleep, the sun has come up on the day I've been dreading, shining through a pattern of patchy clouds that has reminded me ever since, every time I see a similar sky, of my feelings of doom that morning. It's made worse by the fact that it's earlier than I usually wake up, and I feel slightly sick as I get in my car to drive to the church. I know I'm going to die on the stage, and falling apart in performance before friends will be so humiliating that I'm going to have to begin attending another church. At least I can say I tried it, and when I collapse on the platform they'll understand why I'll be telling them never again.

I arrive early to run the music with the pianist. Then I sit down in trepidation, and the service starts. My name is in the bulletin, and my time approaches inexorably like the hangman approaching the lever. The noose is around my neck, and flight is no longer an option, so going through that allegorical trapdoor is the only way out. Now it's the hymn before my solo, and I stand with the rest of the crowd, tunelessly mouthing the words without comprehension.

And then my time comes. On surprisingly steady legs with head held high, I walk up to the stage, nod to the accompanist, and play one of the best performances of my life with all thought of failure forgotten. Many come to me afterward and tell me they hope I'll do it again. An hour ago I would have said absolutely not, no way. The huge leap from the expectation of unavoidable failure to the confidence in dreams of future success is a psychological leap that would be incomprehensible to anyone who hasn't been there themselves.

This happened some years ago, and today, as I gain performance experience, these fears are slowly fading into the past. But old fears take time to overcome and maybe never go away entirely. I'm not unique—I realize this is something every performer faces, and I wrote this hoping others might get a chuckle from it and perhaps some reassurance. I'm not really the one to offer advice, but I think the key to overcoming is when I began to realize that those who hear me do actually enjoy listening. Insights I can suggest are these: play music you enjoy, practice until you know the music well, have faith in your audience, and trust yourself. Unless you play at Carnegie Hall, the audience isn't judging you. And perhaps remember this: "Perfection is the enemy of pretty good."

Intro to
"The Lonely Dreamer"

O f all the things I've written, "The Lonely Dreamer" is the story that flowed off my fingertips the most easily. It isn't autobiographical, but it's a concept I found easy to create. It starts out sounding like a cheap romance story, but keep reading—that isn't what it is at all.

My theme is a late-in-life emotional self-discovery featuring an out-of-shape fifty-eight-year-old man named Howard Midlin with severe self-doubts who invents an imaginary world of greatness and accomplishment to escape the tedious and disappointing reality of his life. If this reminds you of Walter Mitty, I'll admit the concept was inspired by that. He is married to a woman whom he loves still and who loves him, but they've become emotionally separate because of his insensitivity and lack of emotional confidence. Howard sways back and forth through a dizzying confusion of images that he conjures up in his mind to avoid the responsibility for his own failures, and the story culminates with his discovery at age 58 that he doesn't have to be a failure. The genus of that discovery is the real story; the follow-on is left to the reader to imagine.

Howard's mind is free to lurch abruptly from fantasy to fantasy because his world is entirely in his mind, and it lacks any semblance of consistency. That makes it confusing to the reader, but if you're confused, you've gotten the point. If you're inclined to read this all the way through, keep that in mind and understand that there is the beginning of a resolution at the end. Skip to the end if you wish, but it won't make sense unless you follow Howard through that imaginary world of his.

The Lonely Dreamer

Howard Midlin walked along the white sandy beach at the edge of the water with the warm wavelets making eddies around his feet. He was nude, and his strong, masculine physique and bronzed skin glowed in the late-afternoon sun. The sandbar that protected this beach kept the heavy surf away, and the air was quiet except for the distant roar of the sea against the bar. The heat of the afternoon was beginning to abate with the sinking sun, promising a comfortable evening. Ahead, he could see the little seaplane drawn up on the sand, and down the beach a short distance, Carolyn's lithe and womanly figure was walking toward him.

They never wore clothes here, and Carolyn, bronzed as Howard was, filled him with a tender feeling as he watched her graceful movement in the natural setting. They came here so often that they had become accustomed to being without clothing and gave no more thought to it, and the temperature was so perfect it was easy to forget they had nothing on. They spent whole weeks here, lying in the sun and soaking in the warm water and sleeping under the stars and the moon. The small island was so far from the coast that they always had the place to themselves, unafraid of being disturbed, but in the seaplane it was a short flight, and they were able to come here often.

They met on the sand where a large blanket was spread out, the place where they had spent most of the afternoon. They could lie in the sun for hours without fear of sunburn because their skin was so well tanned. Carolyn pressed herself against Howard as he wrapped his strong arms around her. She leaned her cheek against his chest and, after a moment, turned her face to his and accepted a long, tender kiss. Howard had held her just like this so many times, but he never tired of feeling her slim, strong body in his arms. Carolyn felt so safe with him and so loved.

Howard gazed at Carolyn's elegant face in the warm sunlight and remembered how she gave up a brilliant stage and film career for him. He owned a thriving air-charter business that was often engaged to fly celebrities around the world, and she found herself on one of Howard's jets. The Academy selected Carolyn as Most Promising Newcomer the year before, and she had been traveling on a series of engagements as a result of that honor. Howard still flew the charters himself occasionally, and by coincidence he had taken Carolyn's flight himself that morning, at first not recognizing the name of the passenger. Carolyn boarded the plane and was met by the most handsome and manly individual she had ever seen, and she had been struck by his down-to-earth manner and pleasant sensitivity, qualities so unexpected in her line of work. He was wearing an ordinary business suit, not a crew uniform, and she assumed he must be some producer she hadn't met, so she was surprised when he stepped into the captain's seat at the time of departure. From that day forward, they had been inseparable, and she found in him something that replaced the thrill of performing many times over.

"Howard, don't use up all the hot water! I've still got to start the laundry."

Howard opened his eyes, and the beautiful beach, the seaplane, and Carolyn faded into the shabby bathroom like a popped balloon. It seemed fantasies were all he had these days. He had always found it hard to ask Hellen for the love he had once longed for, and these days she so often was out of sorts that he never considered it anymore. In his myopic view of himself he didn't understand that she found him tedious and absent-minded. After a moment, he leaned forward and shut off the hot water that he had been running intermittently to warm the water since he started his bath.

"And don't forget we have to go to Rod and Carolyn's tonight, so get your bath done in time for me to get the laundry started." She muttered to herself, "At fifty-eight he still lolls in the tub for hours and hours and uses up all the hot water."

Howard hadn't forgotten, and his wife's reminder annoyed him. It seemed to him she had gotten more condescending lately, but he hadn't figured out that it was because he did seem to forget things a lot.

"He's so absent-minded," Hellen said to herself. "I wonder if it's Alzheimer's. I should call the doctor."

Howard closed his eyes one more time, but Hellen's raspy interjection had driven away his lovely dream, and as he hefted his pasty and out-of-shape mass out of the warm water he caught himself in the mirror, and he didn't look like the Howard of his fantasies. Maybe he should renew his health-club membership. But then Hellen would probably complain about the cost of membership anyway, so what was the use. He could hear her now. "What's the use? You never go there anyway."

It turned out there was a real Carolyn, but she didn't look anything like the Carolyn in the dream. In fact, she was almost the twin of his wife. But she had once laughed politely at one of his attempts at humor, and from that he allowed himself to imagine that she was attracted to him. He didn't seem to understand that Hellen was always there for him, but relations with her had become strained over the years by the burden of emotional trash that often accumulates between married people, and out of selfishness and insensitivity he had begun to fixate on Carolyn.

Howard dried himself and put on clean underpants and went into the bedroom to find some nice clothes. He reminded himself that Carolyn was just a friend, but down inside, he really wanted to impress her. He found his favorite Hawaiian shirt, the khaki pants that he wouldn't admit were too tight, and a black belt with a large gold buckle that he pretended made him look like Charlton Heston. *The new Charlton Heston,* he had once thought of himself.

Hellen, having finally started the wash, came in just then and didn't waste any time telling him he looked totally fat in those pants, and why on earth did he insist on wearing them when there was another perfectly good pair in the closet that fit better. "And that Hawaiian shirt...do you think we're going to Maui?" She slipped off the old house dress she was wearing, and Howard looked at her out of the corner of his eye. He had once found her appealing, but age and weight and the familiarity that comes from long acquaintance had dulled that. Now Carolyn! There was a relationship free of judgment. He was sure they were made for each other.

They left the house and went out into the hangar. Howard settled into the left seat, and Hellen pulled open the right door and climbed up the step to the right seat. This model of the big De Havilland Beaver had the optional left door, which made it easier for the pilot to get in without disturbing the passengers. He really preferred the jet for its speed and comfort, but it was not able to land on Rob and Carolyn's short grass strip. The Beaver was made famous in the movie *Six Days and Seven Nights* starring Harrison Ford, and in fact, it was interesting to note that this particular airplane was the one used in the movie. Someone asked him once if he had also been the pilot. Howard, being professionally modest, replied it was someone else.

Howard pushed the button to open the hangar door and was most of the way down the starting checklist by the time Hellen got aboard. He moved the mixture control to "rich," turned on the magnetos, and turned the magneto switch to the start position. One blade, two, and it caught, with its familiar throbbing idle. He let it warm up for a moment, then selected reverse pitch, and backed the airplane out of the hangar. Many Beaver pilots refused to use reverse pitch to back up because the operation required unusual skill because of the tail-wheel design, but Howard pioneered the technique himself years before and was admired by many pilots for his mastery.

Howard taxied to the main runway, running down the takeoff checklist on the fly. He contacted the tower, opened up, and the big plane accelerated down the long strip. Before the midpoint it was airborne already. The Beaver with the big radial engine was a high-performance machine, not like the jet, perhaps, but it was an airplane for professionals.

Hellen, always interfering, suddenly blurted out, "Howard, why do you always put the heat on full like that?" and reached out and pushed the mixture control back to "lean." It annoyed him the way she always had to butt in, but after many years of dealing with temperamental passengers he had learned it's often best to just humor them. He knew, after all, that once in flight the mixture was automatic anyway, and the position of the lever didn't matter.

The short flight was routine, and Howard's mind wandered to thoughts of Carolyn. He was so conflicted between the image of her in his fantasy and the reality of his wife that he almost missed the localizer at the field where Rod and Carolyn lived, and he had to let down faster than he liked.

Hellen noticed the lapse and said, "Turn here."

Howard had already noticed, and it annoyed him to be reminded. He slipped it in like the pros do and taxied in one smooth motion to the ramp in front of the house. With a final burst of power, he slid the tail into the narrow parking slot, set the brakes, shut off the lights and radios and heater, and shut down the engine.

Carolyn came to the door right away, and Howard looked discreetly to see what she was wearing. He hoped she would notice him, but she greeted Hellen first with enthusiasm and a hug and glanced at Howard with a short hi. Rod, the owner of the studio and producer and director of this film, shook his hand with his eyes averted and offered him a beer. Howard didn't like to drink when he was working, but he accepted the beer all the same. He could handle it, unlike some others. Looking around, he noticed that other famous cast members were not present, reflecting on how they tended to come in near camera time like prima donnas after making everyone wait. He himself was appreciated in the industry, as many old-timers are, for arriving early and having his lines learned before the filming started.

He didn't like beer, but he sat down at the end of the couch and sipped, trying to act nonchalant and manly as if he drank beer every day. Presently, one of the others joined him, a guy named Gerry, who Howard met once before, at the picnic where Carolyn laughed at his joke. Funny how memories hinged around those sorts of experiences. Gerry asked Howard if he was a fan of the local team, and that was followed by a conversation about baseball, which Howard considered somewhat tedious, mainly because he knew so little about sports that it made him feel stupid. Trying to find something Howard knew about, Gerry let the conversation morph into fishing and hunting with no more success than he had with baseball.

Gerry always found Howard uninteresting and distracted, and he took it as stupidity, and he turned to another man, Bob or Jim or something, who seemed to know more about sports, while trying to include Howard while talking to Bob or Jim, and Howard began to feel left out, which was a very familiar feeling. After all, few of his movie-business colleagues understood that men like Howard prefer not to hold idle conversation when they're focused on their work.

He was rescued by Hellen who came around just then to remind him that there were hors d'oeuvres. He didn't know what that was, but he stood and followed her to the buffet table and filled a plate with various things that looked to him uninteresting but edible. One of the other women started talking to Hellen, and Howard, rudderless once again, turned away from the buffet to examine the various works of art that Rod and Carolyn had on display in their living room.

Howard was an acknowledged expert on a wide variety of subjects, and he frequently lectured on all forms of art. His long experience made him unique among his colleagues for the breadth of his knowledge, and he was frequently sought out for advice. In fact, the Louvre had recently asked him for help with a Picasso they had just purchased; Howard helped them determine which side was the top of the painting.

Moving first to the mantel, mainly because it moved him away from the other people, he found one of the more unique forms of art he had ever seen, something that was quite rare in its creative insight and artistic style. This sort of thing was unusual in private homes because it wasn't pretty in the aesthetic sense, and it took great sophistication to understand its meaning. The object was white, leather in appearance, a simple spherical shape of a size that would fit easily in the hand. It was decorated with brown-and-green splotches like dirt scuffed into the white surface. Passing around the spherical shape in a curving fashion was what appeared to be a stitch pattern of red thread zigzagging back and forth across a seam in the white surface in a way that appeared to hold the outer covering in place.

Howard stood a few minutes, pondering the white sphere. He remembered something similar in a museum in Florida called the Sports Hall of Fame Museum, where he was invited to deliver a series of lectures on the subject of art as related to American sports tradition. He mused that there was a tremendous amount of art that reflected the American passion for sports, some of it quite unique and very modern in its modality, with variations on reality ranging from realistic to highly impressionistic. That museum was founded by one of Howard's colleagues to house an extensive collection, and something like this white orb—in fact, almost identical—was displayed there. Howard wondered if perhaps this example might be a copy of that one, but as he studied it, he realized that it was indeed the same original piece he observed in Florida. He knew that that had been an unusually valuable piece and so well loved that many copies were made. He wondered how Rod and Carolyn obtained this, the original. Howard himself actually owned one of the copies at one time, when he was quite young in fact, and that was probably one of the seeds that led to his extensive interest in art.

And then he noticed a small note next to the white orb, "Danny's first home run," and he knew for sure that this was that same work. Danny, of course, referred to the American artist Daniel Mantle who was famous in midcentury for his abstracts of American sports. Mantle, in fact, had a brother who had been famous as a baseball player. He tended to create things in spherical shapes, which Howard learned was intended to mimic the Earth, with the theme of linking the Earth to American sports in a way that transcended differences between the temporal and the spiritual. Howard discovered this in an interview with the artist himself. Mantle was known among art historians as a recluse, and getting access to him had required Howard's unique interpersonal skills and insights.

And then, Howard caught his breath when he noticed the piece next to the white orb. He stood for a moment looking at it, trying to comprehend that this piece was here in Rob and Carolyn's house. It was a simple drawing on coarse paper stock, with light-blue horizontal lines at regular intervals down the sheet and three holes in the left edge. It was a figure of a woman rendered in green in a simple childlike manner. She appeared to be smiling, looking straight at the viewer. Over her head was a yellow circle with a similar smiling face upon it, with projecting rays of the same color, and in the background was what appeared to be a house with one door and one window rendered in blue. The simplicity of the piece struck him as only a real expert could appreciate. It was reduced to the simplest possible elements, just the woman, the sun, and the house, with simple feelings expressed in the smile, the rays of the sun, and the feeling of security embodied in the house in the background.

At the bottom was the inscription *Mommy*, and Howard remembered his own study of this painting during his year in Provence studying the works of van Gogh. *Mommy* sounds to English-speaking people like the word a child uses for *mother*, but Howard had discovered that van Gogh derived that word from a distortion of the Dutch word *mome*, which connoted a combination of feelings of love, security, home, and warmth. In fact, during this period, the artist adopted the practice of not signing his works with his name but merely with some inscription related to the theme of the work, such as the word *mommy* in this one. During this period of his life, van Gogh created a series of works related to the concepts of love and security, and as all historians know, that period had been labeled as his "security period." Howard studied this series of paintings and found they evoked deep feelings in himself, one of the traits of great art. In fact, he lectured at the Louvre on this very painting during that year abroad, and his discoveries, based in part on his own study of van Gogh's personal diaries, virtually revolutionized the art world by his discoveries of the artist's life and thoughts.

He stood for a moment, studying the small painting, really only a drawing in crayon. Van Gogh had possessed an uncanny ability to incorporate such meaning with such simplicity. This couldn't be the original, could it? It was well-known in the art world that the original disappeared from the Louvre in recent years and was never found. It was sometimes hard to discern a copy from the original, but as he studied the piece, Howard began to realize, from the texture of the lines in the drawing, that, unbelievably, this must be the original. This painting represented such a loss to the world of art, and he realized he had now found it, here in this unlikely place.

And then it took his breath away. In the corner, behind a large recliner, almost as if it were being concealed, was the painting he never dreamed he'd find in a private home. Only here in the Rod's film studio might something this exotic be found. It was an oil by Monet, Howard knew, one painting in a thousand that collectors consistently lust after. The composition was really very simple, almost trivial to the uninformed observer, but with a depth of meaning that only one like Howard could appreciate.

The colors were dark, mainly greenish, with highlights in contrasting colors and with a texture that was smooth with little hint of the strokes of the brush. The lines were crisp and regular, and few of the lines in the painting were straight. The painting showed a green olive with stick-like arms and legs, seated on a barstool, with a single red pimento in the center of the forehead as if intended to resemble an eye. Behind the olive was a long table that most casual viewers would think resembled a bar, and the olive was leaning one arm over the edge of the long table in a jaunty pose. On the table there appeared a martini glass, half full, with a swizzle stick and an olive in the glass. The olive had a similar red pimento. Only those items appeared in the painting and nothing more, and the simplicity of the piece conveyed depth of meaning in a way that no other artist ever achieved. In the lower corner were the initials of the artist, CM, obviously for Claude Monet, and the title of the piece, "Olive Seated on a Barstool." Howard had written, in an analysis of the painting that was published in several journals, that the theme of the piece was the age-old question of whether the glass is half full or half empty.

As Howard was still catching his breath, he began to wonder how Rod and Carolyn came by such an unusual treasure. He considered asking Rod about it; in fact, he was turning to speak to Rod who had been standing right behind him talking to someone else, when another guest, whose name Howard forgot, interrupted his thoughts.

The man found Howard staring blankly at a piece of cheap art won in a raffle on a cruise ship somewhere as if unaware that food was available, and he asked, "Howard, have you had any brats or burgers yet? They're out on the grill in the back."

Howard pretended he had of course known that even though he hadn't, and he moved toward the patio door and stepped into the bright light outside. The camera operator was already setting the focus, and the light crew was making final adjustments. Carolyn was standing near the grill, and Rod, who was directing, producing, and acting in the film, was holding a spatula, waiting for the crew to complete preparations. Interestingly, Rod was playing a character of the same first name. Several extras were placed strategically around the small patio, standing such that the principals were not obstructed in the scene. Howard knew that they had already rehearsed this scene several times using a body double for himself, and some preliminary filming had been accomplished without dialogue. Now they brought him onto the set to do the close-ups and deliver the spoken lines.

Howard had a reputation in the industry for an ability to do things in one take. In fact, they sometimes called him One-Take Howard. He had a knack for clear understanding of what the director wanted, and he even had an uncanny ability to anticipate the dialogue without a glance at the script.

In position now, Carolyn handed Howard a paper plate with a bun. Howard waited for the camera to start and then moved toward the grill. Rod glanced at him with a half smile and placed a brat on Howard's bun. The moment came for Howard to deliver his one line in this scene, and he delivered it with masterful timing, such a simple line yet so significant, another Midlin trademark. The line was "Thanks, Rod," and he was off camera again. The simplest lines were often the most difficult to deliver with conviction. Many experienced actors had trouble with the timing, yet Howard had that sixth sense.

He realized, of course, out of humility that was another of his trademarks, that Rod's small part had been the crucial start for the timing of the scene, and without it, he could not have been as effective. An experienced actor is always respectful of those who perform those important supporting roles.

That scene was done, and he went back into the house and stood at the catering table looking at the hors d'oeuvres feeling alone and depressed while he ate his brat. One or two of the extras tried to engage him in conversation, but a true artist is always distracted after doing a scene, and they found him too preoccupied to make conversation.

Howard picked up some chips and moved away from the table. He glanced through the living room window and saw Carolyn in her calf-length skirt tending to the grill, and he gazed at her while he finished the last of the brat and the chips. Then he looked about to find a place to put the empty plate, and in the process, he wandered down the hall toward the bedrooms.

He was looking for the bathroom thinking there would be a wastebasket there, having missed the wastebasket placed prominently in the living room, but he was thinking about Carolyn and being thus distracted found himself in the master bedroom. He stood for a moment looking at the big bed, and slowly the memory came to him. Carolyn had lain there, her ample but sexy figure wrapped in nothing but a short negligee. She had been asleep, but as Howard entered, her eyes fluttered open, and she looked at him with a loving smile. She rose eagerly and came to him, falling into his embrace and leaning her head against his chest. He wrapped his big arms around her supple figure, and she held him tight around the waist. Gradually the world disappeared, and the walls seemed to turn into pink clouds that closed in about them, and it was hours or minutes or days; even time seemed to stop.

"Howard, what are you doing in Carolyn's bedroom? Don't you know it's impolite to go into people's bedrooms?" Hellen took his arm and pulled him back toward the living room.

He was embarrassed and needed an excuse, and he said, "I had to go to the bathroom."

She said, "Here, give me that dirty plate, and the bathroom is here, not in the bedroom."

He needed to make good his excuse, and he went into the bathroom anyway even though he didn't really need to do anything. His head was still spinning slightly from the unfamiliar alcohol in the beer, and he felt more like going to sleep than rejoining the group. Through the closed door he could hear the hubbub of voices, muffled and blending into a low rumble. After a few moments, he flushed just for effect and came back out.

Howard rarely drank, and when he did, the alcohol made him even more reclusive. Some of the other guests wondered if he was all right, but most of them had seen him like this before and assumed it was normal. They just avoided him because conversation with him was so difficult. He moved back to the buffet noting that as a great actor, he, of course, would be treated with awe, and that it was understandable that the others would give him space. He caught Carolyn's eye just then and tried to give her a quick smile, a smile that he was sure expressed their mutual attraction. She glanced quickly away.

The evening dragged on, and other details, if perhaps illuminating, would make tedious reading. Howard had a higher view of life in general, anyway, and to try to bring himself down to the level of conversation about sports and trivia like that would be contrary to his basic nature. He stood aside and studied the valuable artwork that he knew none of the others could truly appreciate, and let various phrases of creative thought pass through his head, such as *He stood by the edge of the crowd, humble but aloof, observing all things and adding to that mental novel that fills the heads of the most creative of us.*

As the sun went down the filming was moved indoors. There was one more scene yet to be done this evening. It was a very simple scene, the sort of simplicity in the craft that lesser actors could rarely accomplish convincingly. Only a man with the highest sensitivity and sense of timing could give this scene its real power, and Howard knew that this was the reason he had been cast in this role.

Rod, the director, was standing by the door, Carolyn next to him. One by one, the actors were leaving, the camera capturing the moments of departure as each character exited. It was the last scene of the film, something Howard thought of as a curtain-call scene, a finale where all the actors appear, except that in this film, they said farewell one by one, an innovation of Rod's that exemplified his unique directing style. He had some talent, and it might amount to something one day.

Hellen and Howard would be departing midway through the sequence. After all, the principals never leave at the beginning or at the end but always in the middle. That man named Gerry was leaving just ahead of them with a wife Howard for some reason hadn't noticed before, and he and Rod stood for a moment and talked about the next night's game. All around were the signs of a party ending—glasses on tables; small plates everywhere with leftover food; and people, now less numerous, standing while they talked. Carolyn looked their way, first catching Hellen's eye, then glancing at Howard in a way that he wished might be a longing. He so wanted her attention, and in his foggy mind he thought of both of them as well-known celebs exchanging knowing looks.

And now they were in front of the camera. Howard pondered the scene carefully to plan out his delivery and timing. The lights were on. The camera started.

Hellen, having the first line, said, "Well, very nice evening. Thanks so much for having us over!" Such a veteran, that Hellen.

Howard's turn was next. "Thanks, fun party. See you next time." He felt oddly off-balance with his delivery and wished he could do it one more time, but Rod didn't cut the scene, and with Howard's ability he knew it was unlikely anyone would see any fault. When an actor isn't sincere about the line he has to deliver it makes it much harder, but the great ones overcome that.

Howard completed the checklist as Hellen swung aboard. He punched Start on the engine control computer, and slowly the main rotor began to turn. As he waited for it to come up to speed, he reflected that most people of his celebrity status were compelled by their insurance companies to hire professional pilots. Howard, John Travolta, and a small number of others were the few exceptions, and that was based on basic flying skill and experience. Only a man like Howard, or John, who both had tens of thousands of flight hours, could be trusted to fly more safely than a commercial pilot. He had seen every possible situation many times and had flown virtually every type of aircraft.

Hellen, ever the busy body, said, "Howard, let's go. Why are you waiting?"

Non pilots never understand that all the parameters have to be in the green, but Howard knew that explanations never help the uninitiated and kept quiet. Finally he rocked the cyclic to the rear to move the big helicopter slightly backward for clearance and then pulled collective and lifted slowly away.

Hellen was in bed already when Howard finished brushing, and as he came into the bedroom in his PJ's he could see her substantial figure under the covers. He turned back the covers on his side and slid in. Bedtime protocol had been the same for decades: lights off, under the covers, on your back, and you have to say good night to be sure it's agreed that it's time to sleep. And then he lay there for a few minutes, filled with a profound sense of irrelevance that came to him more often these days.

As he lay in the gathering quiet thinking about the day, his dream life suddenly began to seem empty, things he refused to let go of that gave him nothing in return, just clouds and vapors that could fly away. His fantasies of Carolyn and the jet and his movie career began to fade into unreality like all his other dreams, the racing driver, the rock-and-roll drummer, the ballroom dancer, the ship captain. He had clung to those because they sustained him through decades of tedium and mediocrity, but as the years passed they became more and more difficult to hold on to, and the only thing left was a lifelong wish that he was more than the ordinary man he knew he really was. And then, with sudden clarity, the insight came to him that the loneliness didn't have to be.

Howard stepped outside himself and looked in, and the feeling he got upon observing himself was a vague embarrassment, a sense of opportunity long lost, and a feeling of uselessness. In the quiet night it became clear that the only thing he had that was tangible was Hellen, his wife, who he knew he had disappointed but who he realized he loved even still. There was a side of him that wished for more, something real, something he had always been afraid of, but somehow that load of emotional baggage always got in the way. He and Hellen hadn't spent much meaningful time together for a long time, but it wasn't due to a lack of interest. Under his mountain of self-doubt, Howard was just afraid to draw close to her.

Hellen expected more from marriage at the beginning, and it had been good in the early years. But in recent decades her husband had become exasperating at times, with an absent mind and few signs of interest. His expressions of affection came almost exclusively in greeting cards. She loved him all the same though, the way only a wife can love a husband, and she hoped that someday they might draw together again.

She lay under the covers, preparing to sleep, Howard's silent shape beside her. It was like that every night the last many years, in the same bed but separate, sleeping with dreams that were forgotten upon waking, an alarm jarring her into another colorless day like the one before. She had become accustomed to that and accepted it.

But tonight, after decades of nights, she felt something long unfamiliar, a signal she had not known since younger days. Howard had always seemed reluctant to ask for her, and a hand placed lightly on the hip had been his timid way of letting her know. This night, after many years and a lifetime of separations, she felt his little signal. She hesitated a moment fearing it might have been inadvertent, but not wanting to ignore it if it wasn't, she turned on her side and reached out to grasp his hand.

Charlie Is Dead

A sign inside the door pointing to the right
Says "Funeral Service for Charlie Peacock."
He was ninety-six.
"He lived a good life," they'll say.
Does that mean he should accept the inevitable?
Or are we merely excusing ourselves
That we're still here?

The casket is open.
We gaze upon Charlie's old face,
Long familiar yet now lifeless,
And oddly younger-looking.
He doesn't look asleep. He looks dead.
What is it about death?
He's still here, yet he's not.
The world of the living is the only thing we know.
Charlie lies here like he's still here,
Yet we know he isn't, and it's confusing

Because we have no reference from experience
For what comes after.

All of us will arrive here someday.
To us whose years are running short,
Our lives seem to have been one long continuous
    line,
An unbroken line from youth,
And we don't sense how old age has caught up with us.
But to a young person, the aged look a huge displace-
    ment away,
Something from a different era.

Charlie must have viewed his own life
Like something that would never end.
It's easy to think that way when the end is indefinite.
He started out as a child,
And now, here he is.
We spend our lives thinking we have time,
Until suddenly, we don't.

The universe has been here for eons unimaginable,
And although to us, in this time-realm, time passes
    slowly,
In comparison, our life spans are tiny and unimportant.
If that's all there is, why do our lives even matter?

THE LONELY DREAMER

Here is the real mystery:
It seems logical that our self-awareness must continue.
How can it be that we live and love;
Go to school; raise families;
Work all our lives;
Deal with hopes and heartaches,
Illnesses and losses;
And then, it just ends?

Why do some live lives of ease and prosperity,
While others suffer without relief?
Is there no compensation?
That we simply dissolve into nothing
Doesn't seem right or fair.

Why are we given the amazing power of human
intellect
Only to have it end with nothing remaining?
The breadth and depth of human reasoning
Is something that few really perceive.
We can understand molecules and universes,
We can land vehicles on other planets
And get pictures back.
Our science can trace time to the very beginning.
As a race, we share complex ideas
And philosophize and create great art.

There is such a vast difference between us
And the next lower animals
That human life seems to be more than merely
An evolutionary adaptation.

In this, there is a vector that points to a higher
        purpose—
Perhaps we're intended to have fellowship with
Some Being that is infinite in its nature.
Is Death's purpose merely to make room for others,
An end to Self only,
Or are we, at the end, taken into that fellowship?

We used to be taught these things,
But now we consider ourselves enlightened.
One wonders what we do expect.
Are we denying something obvious?
If Charlie understood this during life
It was only as in a glass darkly.
But now he has passed on to whatever is next
And he sees clearly the answer
To the biggest question we all ask.

Memories

Early evening;
Suddenly a scent comes
Through the window from nowhere.
Someone is baking bread.

I'm transported decades back,
And I'm a child again, in Gramma's kitchen.
Today she is long gone,
But suddenly, I'm there as she bakes that bread.
She made bread almost every day,
And the memory is unsettling,
Leaving me feeling an emotion
Long unfamiliar.

It's suddenly summer in Des Moines,
And I'm nine again.
Gramma hands me a piece of dough
And smiles and rubs my head.
A pan of water is boiling for corn on the cob.

Through the window, I can see
Grampa in his garden,
Picking the corn for supper.
Dad is helping, sitting on an inverted bushel basket,
Pulling the shucks off the ears.
The green leaves are all around him
On the ground.
I hear their voices faintly
Through the open window.

Beyond is the old garage,
All that's left of the dairy barn,
Shaded by the ancient trees.
It smells of oil and gasoline.
Dirt floor, an old cluttered workbench,
An ancient grinder Grampa used
To sharpen his mower blades.
He called the little riding mower his tractor.

Mom is playing the piano in the parlor.
It's not quite in tune.
After supper, she'll play for Grampa,
Who will want to sing "How Great Thou Art,"
Like he does every night after dinner.
Before that, she'll help fix dinner,
And she'll probably ask me to set the table.

THE LONELY DREAMER

I always hated that.
But Gramma's bread and Grampa's corn
Are compensation for hours (seconds) of toil.

The day's heat is dissipating as the sun goes lower,
And the birds are singing,
Done with their day's work.
The cicadas make a racket,
And somewhere, a dog barks.
The air is still.
In those days, a calm evening was silent;
What was a dirt road is today a busy four-lane.

These memories have languished
For a long time
Because we no longer have any
Reason to go there.
I know it could never be the same.
The old farmhouse is still there,
Even though someone else lives there now.
Who knows if it still smells the same,
But the new people are establishing
Memories for their own grandchildren.

The Guide

They say that flying is 99 percent boredom and 1 percent sheer terror, and from forty years of experience I can confirm the truth of that. Most pilots get in trouble some time in their lives from negligence or poor judgment, but young pilots are especially prone to that sort of error, and I was once young myself. That's how we learn, I guess.

Early in my flying career, in one of those moments of terror caused by my own lack of good judgment, I had an odd experience that I've never been able to explain. In all my flying years I still haven't decided what to make of it, so I'll put it down here just as it happened and let you decide for yourself.

My hometown was Bellville, Michigan, which is a working-class town about twenty miles west of Detroit. I moved to the Chicago area for my first job after college graduation, and for Christmas that year I took a week's vacation to spend the holiday back home. The old house was conveniently close to Willow Run Airport, and I decided to make the trip in a rented Cessna rather than slogging my way across southern Michigan in my car. My private-pilot license was only a few months old, and I was still inexperienced enough to think that earning the pilot's license would make me invincible.

I was expected back at work on the second, but I made a last-minute decision to head back to Chicago on New Year's Eve. I originally planned to go back on the first in the daytime, but the night sky on New Year's Eve was crystal clear, and the moon was full—exactly the sort of night when pilots most enjoy being aloft. Besides, I thought it would be nice to have the extra day before returning to the office.

I took a taxi to the airport to save my folks the trouble—it being New Year's Eve—and the driver dropped me off about 9:00 p.m. Willow Run had once been the main airport for Detroit, but decades before this story Wayne County Airport was expanded and became Detroit Metropolitan Airport, and Willow Run, being smaller with no more land available for expansion, was reduced to a facility that served corporate, charter, air freight, and private planes. So it was no longer a busy air-carrier facility, and as I had expected for New Year's Eve, the small terminal building on the east ramp that catered to planes like mine was deserted. I walked through and out onto the ramp on the other side, where my red-and-white Cessna 150 glowed under the moon with its red stripes looking dark in the bluish cast of the ramp lights. There was a hint of frost on the wings, but I decided it wasn't enough to brush off. Outside the brightly lit parking area the airport was bathed in a silvery moonlit sheen that lends an air of romance even though it makes a winter night seem colder.

My winter trip in the Cessna had been slightly risky because winters in the Detroit area tend to be cloudy and foggy. I had merely hoped for a high ceiling, but tonight the sky was so obviously clear that I hadn't called for a weather briefing. For a moment, as I walked out across the ramp, I wondered if I should go back inside and call from the phone in the lobby, but it was a chilly walk back to the terminal, and on such a night I didn't consider the weather to be any problem. Besides, if I ran into trouble, I could just turn around and come back. Later I would remember my mom's admonition, "Don't go at night—can't you wait till tomorrow?" but what do mothers know?

My salary that first year was not lucrative, and by the time I reached the airplane I was regretting my decision, made during warm weather, to economize on the jacket I was wearing. It was only a few degrees below freezing, but they had parked me quite far out, and my teeth were chattering by the time I got the wings and tail untied. As I unlocked the cabin door and leaned in to confirm the tanks had been filled, I considered skipping the preflight inspection in favor of getting the engine going to get some warm air in the cabin, but it had been a week, and it didn't seem prudent to take off without at least a quick walk around. Under the moon, I almost didn't need the small flashlight I carried in my pocket, and when I took down the checklist from where I kept it on the glare shield I found I could read it under natural light.

My end of the east ramp was deserted, and I kept thinking the line, *Nothing was stirring, not even a mouse*, from the famous poem my dad read to us every Christmas when we were kids. We hated it because it delayed opening presents. There was a brief sign of life as a turboprop twin landed and taxied to the executive terminal at the other end of the ramp and then the field was quiet again. I heard voices briefly, and I knew there were people over there, but on my end of the ramp I was all alone.

The flight home that New Year's Eve night had been a last-minute decision that didn't allow time to arrange to have the engine preheated, hoping, I suppose, that it would start without it. Cold airplanes are hard to get running, and the specter of a dead battery is a concern on a cold night when no one is around to help. The prop swung sluggishly, but after several tries and lots of prime I managed to convince it to run. The cabin heat in small planes comes off the muffler, so with the engine running I quickly felt the cabin heating up, and soon the shivering stopped.

I brought the RPM up a little and let it run for a few minutes, listening to the gyros spinning up and telling myself I was waiting for the oil temperature to rise, which is true, I guess, but in those early days of my flying career I was very radio shy, and really I was putting off my call to the tower. But I couldn't move without calling ground control, so I planned carefully what to say and called for taxi clearance. There was no wind, so they cleared me to two-seven for a straight-out departure to the west, and as I picked my way between the blue taxiway lights I told myself I was being a real pro.

The Cessna lifted like a kite, and I headed west toward the university town of Ann Arbor, home of the Wolverines, which marks the western edge of the sprawl of lights that defines the greater Detroit area. Jackson came into sight thirty miles ahead and a little to the right, and a few smaller towns appeared as small orange pools. I had laid out my planning sheets and maps on the other seat, and I picked up the chart to find the frequency for the radio beacon at Litchfield, Michigan. I centered the needle and turned southwest. Ten miles out the tower called to give permission to change frequency, and to preserve the peace and quiet I turned the radio off.

It's hard to put into words the feelings of flying on a night like this. The snow-covered ground was brightly lit by the moon, and beyond the city lights of the Detroit suburbs the bluish sheen was almost like day. Blue farm lights were scattered here and there, and roads appeared as slim black lines with occasional headlights moving with unnatural slowness. Just past Ann Arbor, still climbing, I saw a farmer with a scampering dog, very small from my height, walking across a floodlit farmyard toward a house with brightly lit windows, signs of warmth and family life within. The house had colored Christmas lights along the edge of the roof. You know how a tune can get stuck in your head. The song "Joy to the World" had been playing at my parents' house when the cab picked me up that evening, and as I gazed downward at the snow-covered landscape I kept hearing that song over and over. Warm air flooded in through the cabin's heat system; the hum of the engine gave me a sense of security, and despite my altitude, I felt a connection with the earth beneath. Just then, if I could have known that this trip would last forever, I would have been content.

I rarely flew the 150s very high because they climbed so slowly, but I wanted to be high on a night like this just for the view, and I climbed all the way to 6,500 before leveling off. I set up for cruise power, glanced at the engine gauges, and settled back to enjoy the trip. It took about a half hour to reach my first waypoint at Litchfield, and another thirty-five minutes to the second course change south of Elkhart, Indiana. Considering where I was headed, that route is a little circuitous on the map, but a direct route from Willow Run would have taken me over Lake Michigan where the unexpected could result in a landing in the water. That's one good decision I made on this trip anyway.

But I mentioned before that flying is 99 percent boredom. It's ironic that by the time I got to Elkhart

I had begun thinking about all the things I needed to do when I got back to work. Flying still seemed romantic to me in those early days of my flying career, but I began to sense that at times it could be a lot like driving a car—sometimes there isn't much to do but sit there and wait for the next navigational checkpoint.

As I made the course change near the sea of lights that marked the area around Elkhart and South Bend, Lake Michigan came slowly toward me out of the northwest to the right of my course. From aloft it looked like a black half oval, slowly expanding, ringed by the luminous whiteness of the moonlit landscape, with towns and cities wrapped around the shoreline that in my Pollyanna mentality of that night resembled a string of Christmas lights. *How lucky I was,* I thought, *that I was able to fly, free of traffic and tolls and all the slow hassle of traveling on the surface.* It's strange that I could be judgmental on such a night, but below me I could see headlights moving along Interstate 80, and I couldn't help thinking that losers drive and real men fly.

And then the world disappeared.

It was sudden and completely unexpected, and my first reaction was denial. The memory went through my head of riding a motorcycle at night years before when the road descended into a misty hollow and my faceplate fogged over. At first, I thought my eyes had failed, and I blinked to clear them, but I remember looking at the panel and realizing I could still see the instruments. Then with a glance through the left window, I could see the red navigation light shining into mist, and I knew what had happened. In an instant, "Joy to the World" was swept away, replaced by a tuneless blackness and the beginnings of panic as the myriad small concerns of my busy first year of working life were swept into inconsequence. Why I didn't notice the cloud ahead of time, I can't say, but I had been thinking about work and hadn't wondered, I guess, why the lights of the cities around Gary and Calumet and South Chicago weren't visible yet.

At first I hoped the cloud would end quickly, but it didn't, and shortly I began to panic, and then I began to sweat, and very quickly I became confused about the instrument readings. Every private-pilot trainee gets a small amount of instrument train-ing, enough perhaps to understand how to read the instruments, but not enough to go it alone when the shock of unexpected instrument conditions hits. Having earned my instrument rating since then, I can't imagine how I survived this experience with the lack of training I had at the time. I was completely unaccustomed to the discipline of instrument flight, and I struggled to hold it level by the attitude indicator, but I found myself repeatedly correcting the wrong direction. I would catch it as the attitude diverged farther from level flight, but I kept doing it, and I quickly fell more and more behind the airplane. Twice in the first few moments the moon appeared between wisps of cloud, the second time in a completely different part of the sky from the first, and neither place was a place where I knew it should be.

In less pressured circumstances, like driving my car or sitting on the couch in my apartment, I often thought about flying in actual blind conditions, imagining myself calm and collected, perfectly at ease. "Real men" never get confused because "hey, you just read the instruments." Until you've experienced it, it's impossible to understand how vertigo closes like a vise on the unprepared. Without prior practice, finding yourself unexpectedly in actual instrument conditions is a rude awakening, and it's irreversible once it starts.

Soon, I gave up trying to hold altitude and concentrated on just keeping it upright, and with that simplified focus I managed to get it level for a few moments at a time. But I couldn't keep it up—I would get confused by the sensations in my inner ear, and a new wave of vertigo would set in. I would find myself up on one wing with the nose downward, the airspeed rising with a loud rushing along the aluminum skin of the fuselage, and I would fight back level and hold it steady for a few moments again. But the cycles repeated, and the intervals between moments of panic got shorter and shorter. I stared fixedly at the attitude indicator trying to maintain control, but my senses contradicted what the instruments were trying to tell me, and soon I stopped believing the instruments entirely.

In ground school before I started flight training, they showed a film on emergency weather procedures. The narrator intoned with deep authority that if you find yourself unexpectedly in the clouds, make a 180-degree turn by doing a standard rate turn for one minute and then hold that heading until you exit the cloud. What he didn't say was that without proper training you'll get so confused so quickly that you won't even be able to read the clock. I did after a while remember the 180 trick, but when I glanced at the compass the reading didn't register, and it almost certainly wasn't the heading I had been on. I couldn't even remember what my heading had been, and I'm sure my fogged mind wouldn't have been able to figure out the reciprocal heading anyway. At that point, I would have been happy to be merely upright and stable, but I was stuck in the cloud, and I ran out of tricks.

And then another problem cropped up, something my mind in its fogged state could still perceive—the engine began to cough—and suddenly it was running very roughly. I pushed the throttle to the firewall, but the increase in power lasted only a short time before it began to drop again, and as the power dropped off I forgot to watch the airspeed. A loud buzzing sound persisted for some time before it finally caught my attention, and as it sank in I realized it was the stall warning. The airplane was trying to tell me I was going too slow. Somehow, I managed to get the nose down to keep the speed up, but it threw me off-balance again, and vertigo set in worse than before.

The cabin heat began to fall off with the loss of power, but I was soaked with sweat. As the confusion deepened my face began to tingle with the feeling of helplessness, and with the rising fear my vision began to fade. It was the same sensation I felt in my first public-speaking experience except that this time I couldn't just stop and sit down. I was headed for certain impact with the surface but nothing was making any sense—my mind ceased to engage in logical thought. Strangely, in those last few moments, the thought foremost in my mind was that I was going to smash up a rented airplane. The risk to myself seemed unimportant.

The secular environment of college and working life made my religious roots easy to forget. Life seemed easy and I felt no need for Someone Higher, but there is something unique about aviation that reminds us that we are dependent at times on blind luck, and when luck fails, on that Someone Higher. At that moment, the words "Lord, help me" went consciously through my head.

Suddenly, there was a voice, calm and clear but full of authority. The voice said, "Turn on your radio." The voice seemed to come through the radio, but I knew the radio was off. I actually looked over to see if someone was sitting in the other seat. It's funny, after all these years, to remember that the thought that came to my mind was that that person would be sitting on my maps. Utterly drained of any credulity, I managed amidst the confusion to find the switch on the radio. I had no idea what frequency to use.

That unexpected voice shook me back to reality, and although mentally drained beyond the capacity to fly, I began to take stock of the situation once more. I had given up trying to control the plane and Cessna's natural stability caused it to settle into stable flight all by itself, although descending due to the loss of power.

I wondered of course if the voice had been a hallucination, but I heard it again, through the radio this time, "Cessna 18225, can you hear me? Put your hands on the controls."

I suddenly realized that I had heard this same command several times in the last few moments. I felt reassured by the sound of the voice, and I put my hand back on the yoke, but I was afraid to try to take control again for fear of upsetting my current stable situation. The voice came again. "Twenty-two Kilo, this is Skymaster 1492 Charlie. Do you read me? Please acknowledge."

Amazed, I picked up the microphone and spoke awkwardly, "This is Two Two Five. I hear you okay." Real pilots always say "Loud and clear," but I didn't think of that at the time. It also didn't occur to me until long afterward to wonder how he knew my numbers or what frequency my radio was set for.

"How is your engine running?"

"Rough," I replied.

"Put on your carb heat."

The obvious doesn't always come to mind right away—carburetor icing didn't occurred to me in my confusion as the engine began to fail. I reached for the carb-heat knob and pulled it out. There was a delay with more coughing and sputtering, but soon the engine started to run better, and suddenly it smoothed out completely, at full power, because I had pushed the throttle in all the way.

"Throttle back to cruise power and hold your nose level. Watch your attitude indicator." The calm voice in my radio gave me renewed hope, and I resolved to struggle with it again, but I still hadn't recovered the ability to make sense of the instruments.

And then the voice came again. "I am just ahead of you and a little above. Look out your windshield. Use me as a reference and follow. Take care not to overcontrol."

I tore my eyes away from the panel and looked out the front, and there in front and slightly above was the rotating beacon of another aircraft, misty through the fog and stationary in space. Every pilot feels a moment of panic upon seeing another aircraft in such close proximity, but I fought back the impulse to veer away because I had nothing else to guide on.

"I'm turning on my landing light. You'll see my silhouette against the cloud ahead."

Suddenly, the sky ahead was illuminated by a bright light seen through thick haze, and in misty outline I could see the unmistakable silhouette of a Cessna Skymaster.

The cloud was thick and uniform, giving the scene a dreamlike air without any sense of motion. The Skymaster stayed ahead and above, keeping pace exactly, and I followed the black shape like a lost sheep following a shepherd.

Then for the first time, I looked at my altimeter. When my mind finally managed to resolve the reading, I was startled that it read 900 feet. With the ground at 650 I had been less than a minute from hitting the ground when the Skymaster found me.

The other pilot spoke again. "You should be on a flight plan if you're going to fly on a night like this. You're lucky—tonight, at least, there's no danger of collision. No one is up in these conditions, especially on New Year's Eve." He paused, and I asked him how he found me. He ignored the question, asking instead, "Are you a new pilot?"

I told him about the 110 hours in my logbook. He asked, "Did you call for a weather briefing before you took off?"

I admitted I hadn't; the weather had been perfect on the other side of the state.

He said, "Never fly around the south end of the lake without calling Flight Service first. I made a mistake like that once, and it only takes one time."

By then, I had the presence of mind to ask where we were. He told me we were ten miles east of Coralville, Indiana, and he had picked me up on a northbound heading, which would have brought me out over the lake shortly. After a moment he continued, "The cloud goes all the way to the surface. I'll lead you to the runway at Coralville, and you can wait out the weather there. There's also a motel across from the airport if you want a better place to sleep. The fog should clear in the morning. The runway is lighted, and there is fuel on the field."

I acknowledged and settled in to follow in his wake. We droned on through the fog, and I guided on the outline of the Skymaster as I listened to the sound of my engine. Minutes went by, and with nothing to do but stare at the other aircraft, it seemed like a long time. The fog was thick, and I was constantly afraid of losing him, but somehow I managed to stay within sight of his silhouette, maintaining controlled flight by just watching him. I frequently heard his voice through the radio as if making sure I was okay.

It didn't occur to me till the next day that I hadn't been controlling my own speed, yet the Skymaster and I had managed to keep pace exactly. But my position below and behind would have been a blind spot from his vantage point, so he must have been controlling the speed himself. How could he be doing that when there was no way he could see me? If there was another aircraft, surely, I would have heard another voice, but there was nothing else out there. These thoughts became part of the mystery of the whole experience, but I didn't think of that before he interrupted my thoughts again.

"I've brought you back to a westbound heading, and I'm going to continue the turn to the south to intercept the approach to the runway at Coralville. Don't lose me. You'll be landing to the south. Watch your compass—we'll be rolling out on a 180 heading. And watch the altitude—the field elevation is 650."

Watching the other aircraft with no other out-side references, I hadn't been aware of the turn, but a glance at the compass, which I could read this time, indicated we were turning slowly left. After a short while it seemed to me he began a turn to the right, but the compass read south, and after a moment I realized we were actually rolling level out of a left turn.

To prepare me for the approach, he went on. "I'm going to begin the descent. Stay below me, and I'll bring you down to the runway. Don't use your landing light. It'll reflect off the fog, and you won't be able to see anything. Put down 30 degrees of flap. Don't go all the way to 40 because it'll make the landing flare too abrupt. I'll be reducing speed to 70, so slow down with me. You won't see the runway till you're almost down, so I'll descend on a shallow angle so you won't need to flare as abruptly."

The attitude change was gradual, but I had to keep pushing the nose down to counteract the trim change with the flaps. He had slowed, and I began to catch up, and for the first time I had to reduce power to get my speed under control.

"Hold it steady. We're almost there. You're about an eighth of a mile out."

Many seconds went by, and it seemed so much longer than it probably really was that I began to wonder if he had forgotten to tell me we were near the runway. Glancing out the side window, I could still see nothing but blackness, and it seemed we must still be way too high.

And then he said, "Close your throttle but don't let the nose fall. You'll be on the ground any second. A glance at the altimeter confirmed that we should be almost down.

I tore my eyes away from the Skymaster long enough to look out the side, but I still saw no sign of any lights, nothing to give me confidence we were near the runway. He told me earlier that the runway at Coralville was lighted, and I thought I should be able to see the lights dimly at least if we were that close. I began to think that this guy in the Skymaster didn't have any idea where we were—how could he? His sixth sense seemed too miraculous to trust; he couldn't see any better than I could. We might have been out over Lake Michigan for all I knew.

I began to panic again, especially frightened because I was going to have to take control by myself somehow. I was reaching out to push the throttle back to the firewall when there was the solid squeak of tires on pavement, a long bounce, and then a crazy lurch as the wheels planted again. The nose wheel came down with a solid thump, and it was only then that I saw the runway lights going by on each side, almost invisible through the fog, even this close.

I grabbed the throttle and pulled it shut and got my feet on the brakes for fear I might be almost to the end already. In the fog, without my landing light, it was hard to stay on the runway centerline, and I steered a crooked path as I tried to keep it between the lights. I slowed to a crawl, looking ahead for the blue lights of a taxiway, thinking I should get clear of the runway to make way for other traffic. It didn't occur to me just then that the Skymaster would have been the only other traffic.

My guide disappeared from sight as I slowed, and I was left alone in the fog. I couldn't remember his call letters just then, and I picked up the mike and spoke awkwardly.

"Thanks, I appreciate your help."

I heard him reply. "It's okay. Go get your instrument rating and always check weather before you fly! And good luck." I heard his radio click off, and then he came on once more. "Turn left at the taxiway midfield." I assumed I would meet him on the ground in a few minutes, so I put the mike away to concentrate on getting off the runway.

I was suddenly shaking uncontrollably, and when I reached for the throttle my hand missed the knob. I taxied a long way before I found the turnoff, so he must have brought me in right at the threshold.

I spoke through the radio for the sake of the Skymaster, "Coralville traffic, Two Two Five clear of the runway," and followed the blue lights until a lighted ramp and a small airport building material-ized out of the mist close in front of me. I taxied into a corner, pulled the parking brake, and shut every-thing off. I sat a moment to get over the shaking, listening to the gyros winding down, relieved and surprised to find myself safely on the ground.

I popped open the door and stepped out. The step on the gear strut was icy and my foot slipped off, and I leaned against the bottom of the doorframe to hold myself from falling to the pavement. I noticed for the first time a thin coating of ice on the wings. I wondered later why there was none on the wind-shield. I assumed the Skymaster would be coming in right behind me, so I stood there to wait, but five minutes went by, then ten, and he didn't appear. I was disappointed because I wanted to thank him in per-son—the approach had been nothing short of heroic considering the impossible conditions. Later, I looked it up and found there were no instrument approaches to the airport at Coralville, so he must have led me in visually. I've wished ever since that I could have asked him how he did that in that thick fog.

The chill was soaking through my thin jacket, so after a few more minutes I figured he had his own life and continued on to wherever he was going when he picked me up. I pushed the cabin door shut and walked over to the little building. A sign over the door said "Welcome to Coralville Sky Port, world's friendliest airport." The building was unattended, but the door was unlocked, and the dimly lit lobby was warm. A clock on the wall read "11:30." My two hours in the air seemed much longer, and my takeoff from Willow Run seemed like another life ago.

I walked through the lobby to the street door on the other side. Across a small parking lot I could see a wide street, and the fog seemed thinner there, perhaps because of the slight heat from passing traffic. I had expected to sack out on a couch in the airport building until morning, but I could see a Holiday Inn across the street, and it was too inviting to pass up.

I pulled my jacket shut and walked across. In those days, many motels closed their offices late in the evening, and he was just locking up, but he let me in and gave me a room. The shaking still persisted, but at this point it had more to do with hunger. But I was too tired to take the trouble to find a restaurant anywhere, so I bought a candy bar from a machine. I was so fatigued I could hardly walk, and I had a splitting headache, but having reached the bed I found I was not the slightest bit sleepy. I had forgotten to get my little suitcase out of the airplane, so I lay back on the bed in my clothes and reached for the TV remote, and it seemed only a moment later that the clock on the bed table read "3:00." I had fallen asleep so fast I hadn't been aware. My candy bar was still there uneaten. I picked up the remote and turned off the TV and got under the blankets, and when next I woke, it was the maid knocking on the door, and the morning light was streaming through the gaps in the curtain. I had forgotten to put out the Do Not Disturb sign.

I called through the closed door to apologize that I was still in the room and checked the weather through the window. It was still foggy, but there was a hint of blue above. I was ravenous with hunger, and I went to the office where they told me there would be doughnuts and coffee. And then I remembered I promised to call my parents when I got home. There was a pay phone in the lobby, and I could hear the relief in my mom's voice. They had been worried when I didn't answer the phone at my apartment late the night before. I told them I landed due to poor weather and waited it out in Coralville, but I spared them the rest of the details.

At ten the visibility was still poor, but I walked back across to the airport anyway. There was a man in the airport building wearing a name tag that said "Manager," who accepted my six bucks for the parking. He seemed in a surly mood for having to work on New Year's Day, and he chided me a little roughly for not tying the plane down. *So much for world's friendliest airport,* I thought, but I had been so exhausted when I came in the night before I hadn't tried to find a parking spot with ropes.

I called Flight Service and was told that the fog should clear by noon. There was a couch next to a stack of magazines, and I sat down to wait it out. At eleven it still didn't look much like clearing, but I had looked at all the magazines, so I went out and coaxed the plane to life again and taxied to the fuel pumps.

I didn't really need fuel, but it gave me something to do while I waited.

I was met at the pump island by an old man with a deeply lined face who looked old enough to have mentored the Wright brothers. A tag on his jacket said "Robert." He seemed inclined to chat, and as he pulled the fuel hose over he told me that he had been a flight instructor here for thirty-two years until a bad heart forced him to retire, but he still hung around the airport, pumping gas and assisting pilots to give himself something to do. Robert brought a ladder over from behind the pumps and climbed up to get at the gas caps, pausing in his monologue as he started to fill the tanks. They had been nearly half full, which means I still had plenty of fuel to reach my final destination, but I let him fill both tanks anyway. As I turned to go inside to pay for the gas, he said to me, "Might as well leave it parked right where it is—nobody else'll be needing gas till this fog clears."

I paid, and with no more magazines to read, I walked back outside. Robert was sitting on a low fence by the parking lot smoking a cigarette, and he looked up as I sauntered over.

"Some fog," he said, "doesn't very often get this bad, maybe once or twice a winter. Nobody flies when it's like this. No published approaches, not here…way below minimums anywhere in the area, anyway." He looked up at me quizzically. "I don't remember your 150 being here yesterday. When did you come in?"

I told him last night about eleven thirty, and he looked up at me with a quizzical look.

He asked, "Did it clear off late in the evening?"

I couldn't answer without telling him about last night. I had hoped no one would ask because what I had done was completely foolish and a violation of all the rules. I tried to act nonchalant about it all, but suddenly found I was telling him the whole story about the vertigo, how I had forgotten (as I put it) to call for a weather briefing, and how I had been guided in by the mysterious Skymaster.

"That guy was one sharp pilot," I said to him. "He brought me right down to the runway, and I was on the ground before I even saw the lights."

And then I remembered an association that came to mind when the Skymaster told me his numbers on the radio. Robert was silent for a few moments, and from the look on his face, I couldn't tell if 1492C meant anything to him. He dropped his cigarette butt and ground it out under his toe, and then he looked up at me and said, "You sure?"

I told him yes, I was sure. *C* for Columbus and 1492 for the year of his voyage. The association with Columbus had been easy to remember even in my state of mind at the time.

Robert was silent for a long moment, face upward, but eyes downward. Then he caught my eye again with a skeptical look as if he were trying to come to grips with some new and surprising truth. He caught his breath and said, "That can't be. Because if you heard right, that would be Floyd Benson's plane. Floyd wouldn't have been up last night, of that I'm sure. Nor would his airplane."

I was surprised that he knew the pilot and asked him to explain. He paused for a moment as if trying to decide what to say, as he got another cigarette from his shirt pocket. He sucked on it a few times as he lit it with a butane lighter, blew some smoke, and then continued, "Floyd was a student of mine about five years ago. He had some money—he ran some sort of a business here in town. He was rather slapdash as a beginner, and I almost booted him out of my school because I was afraid he'd wreck my Cherokee. But I got him settled down, and he learned as quick as any student I ever had, and he got real good real fast. I let him solo at six hours, fastest I've ever seen." He paused, staring into the fog, then continued. "I trained him in my Cherokee 140—that one parked on the grass over there. I had to sell it because I couldn't afford to keep it after I lost my medical, and the guy that bought it leases it back to the flight school. It's still used for training and rentals.

"Anyway, Floyd got bored with trainer planes, and he wanted something faster. He hadn't even finished training for his private license before he bought that old Skymaster, Niner-Two Charlie, or Columbus, if you like. Barely flyable, but the price was right. We had to put new magnetos on the rear engine before I'd teach him in it, and I wasn't happy with it even then. The first annual was real expensive, and Floyd almost wished he hadn't bought it. But he kept it, and he liked flying it, and I taught him in it, and he got his centerline thrust rating as soon as he could after he got his private. His insurance wouldn't let him solo in it till he had twenty-five hours of twin time, so I rode around with him till he accumulated that many hours. After that, he flew that eggbeater a lot, and he really thought he was hot stuff. Raindrops would sizzle when they fell on his head!" Robert grinned and then got serious again. "That's the sort of guy Floyd was. I worried every time I saw him fly."

That story had me confused because I didn't know what the point was. I knew that 1492C had indeed been up the night before, but I didn't want to push too hard for fear of causing offense. Robert must have read my mind because he looked at me with that strange look again.

He said, "Those were Floyd's numbers for sure, but I'm sure it wasn't Floyd—he can't fly anymore or do anything else, for that matter. Floyd went up late one afternoon just before Christmas three years ago, and it turned into one of those nights just like last night. I watched him take off, and I didn't see him get back before the weather closed in. He didn't bother to call Weather because it was just a local flight, and it looked good when he went up. I didn't hear anything, and I assumed he must have gotten down somewhere, but the weather cleared the next morning, and by evening he still wasn't back, so the guy who managed the airport called the police and reported him missing."

He looked down at his shoes for a moment and kicked a small stone into the grass. "We didn't hear anything for several days, and then we got a call from the sheriff. A farmer found the wreck and called the authorities, and it was so destroyed he didn't even know it was an airplane, just a pile of scrap aluminum with what was left of Floyd still in his seat. He came down nose first into a grove of trees about ten miles east of here. He must have hit really hard because the weight of the rear engine crushed the cabin. Both tanks were destroyed, but there was fuel in the lines still, so he wasn't out of gas, but somehow there wasn't a fire. They pulled the engines and tore them down for inspection. They both had plugs fouled real bad with carbon, so he must've had a bad case of carburetor ice."

The old man was looking down, and his face was thoughtful and sad, and I remained silent to let the feelings play out. But I felt a bit embarrassed for my old friend because I knew I had seen 92C alive and well just last night. Either Robert was getting old, or he had his numbers mixed up. In college and in flight school I had been thoroughly trained to be objective, and this conversation was getting hard to take at face value. Dead men don't just reappear to help a lost pilot home.

Robert stopped speaking, and I stood there wondering how to extricate myself without seeming disrespectful. Then looking down at his shoes, he went on in a quiet voice. "I heard another story like that once. A fellow was guided into Gary one night a year ago when there was thick fog like we had last night…. 'The other plane didn't land,' he said, and he forgot the call letters. But I was in the hospital then with my bad heart, and I never learned any other details. I figured it was just a rumor."

He gazed into the distance as he took a last drag on his cigarette, and then he said, "Well, I gotta…," and he stood and went inside.

And then I remembered the other pilot's comment, where he said he made the same mistake once, and it only takes one time…

By noon the fog had lifted into a thin overcast, and by one the sun was shining. Having learned from the experience of the previous night, I called Flight Service for a weather briefing, but they confirmed it was clear all the way. The hellish flight through the cloud seemed distant and unreal, but I've never forgotten what I learned—real men don't assume they're invincible.

Memories often fade as the decades pass, but that New Year's Eve flight remains clearly etched in my mind, and despite my confused state that night I still remember the smallest details. I'm always skeptical when I hear stories like the one I've just told, and I've tried to explain it every way I could, but nothing in my increasingly many years has given me any rational basis for the events of this story. My mind goes around and around in a circle, and that circle always ends at the same place—that almost involuntary prayer just before I heard the voice of 92C on the radio. When something can be explained by physical phenomena one needn't turn to mysticism or theology, but in this case I'm at a loss to explain it any other way.

I understand the skepticism of anyone who might read this, but that pilot, whatever he was, was my guide, and he led me to safety under impossible conditions. My flying career should have been cut short that New Year's Eve because of my own poor decision-making, but I lived to fly these forty more years because he was there to help.

About the Author

David Clark is retired from a career as a mechanical engineer and writes as an avocation. He was an airplane owner for many years and is currently active as an orchestra musician, two themes that appear in his writing. He was born in Boston and grew up in Michigan and has been living in Minnesota for nearly fifty years. He is married to Connie Fukuda-Clark, and he and Connie have two bratty but affectionate Cavalier King Charles spaniels. This book is his first published work.

Milton Keynes UK
Ingram Content Group UK Ltd.
UKHW040836160724
445389UK00001B/2